LARGE PRINT

SHIVA

THE DESTROYER OF ALL EVIL

OM
Om Books Internation...

Shiva and Sati

Daksha Prajapati was a powerful king. He had sixteen daughters, and his wife—Prasuti— was the daughter of Manu.

One day, Daksha's wife came to him with a request. "My Lord! Don't you think we are not paying attention to our growing daughters? They are of marriageable age and we have not found a worthy husband for even one of them," she said.

Daksha had already made up his mind. "I will give thirteen of my daughters in marriage to Dharma. The fourteenth one will wed Agni, the god of fire and the fifteenth will wed the Pitris," he announced. "Then that leaves Sati, our youngest daughter," said Prasuti. "Does Sati like

anyone?" asked Daksha. "I am not sure. She is very different in her ways. When all our other daughters are playing, she sits in front of Shiva's idol and worships him," replied Prasuti.

As Daksha and Prasuti were discussing the future of their daughters, sage Narada entered. "Daksha, you need not put much thought to Sati's future. She is destined to marry Lord Shiva," he said.

Daksha was not happy with Shiva as his son-in-law as he thought that Shiva had no

riches to his name like other gods. He wore only a tiger skin and smeared his entire body with ash. “There is nothing attractive about

him," he thought. But Sati's devotion and sheer love for Shiva forced him to give his daughter in marriage to Shiva. Sati and Shiva were married in a grand ceremony attended by all the gods.

Soon after, Marichi—a great sage—and others performed the famous Brahma Satra yagna (an event where offerings are made to the holy fire). Each one of the gods and kings were present at this holy event. Shiva and

Brahma were seated on a throne. As the yagna was being conducted, all eyes turned to the door. Daksha had made a grand entrance! Everyone present at the event stood up in respect to Daksha. But Shiva and Brahma remained seated.

Daksha was annoyed with his son-in-law for not showing him respect. “While everyone stood up, he remained seated. He thinks he is superior to me!” thought Daksha. “I will now perform a yagna even bigger than this and insult him by not inviting him to it,” he decided.

Daksha performed the yagna to which only Shiva was not invited! But Sati desired to attend it. "My Lord! I would like to attend my father's yagna, and I think you should also come with me," she told Shiva. "Sati! Your father thinks that I insulted him by not standing up at Marichi's yagna. So he has intentionally not invited us," replied

Shiva. "Why should we be invited? We are family to him," said Sati with disgust. Shiva knew that his words were falling on deaf ears. So he asked Sati to proceed to the

event without him. He sent his ganas—followers—with her.

But Sati was in for a surprise. Just like Shiva had said, Daksha was furious to see her. "Why have you come here without being invited?" he demanded. Sati could not bear the insult. So she stepped into the holy fire and soon turned into ashes. The news of Sati's death reached

Shiva. In his anger, he tore a strand of his hair, and from it rose a powerful demon called Veerabhadra. "Veerabhadra, go and destroy Daksha and his yagna," thundered Shiva.

Veerabhadra and Shiva's followers destroyed the complete yagna. Veerabhadra severed Daksha's head from his body. The ones who survived ran to Lord Vishnu and Lord Brahma. "Lord! We beg for mercy!" they cried.

Vishnu and Brahma, in turn, went to Kailash and pleaded with Lord Shiva to pardon Daksha for his mistake. The kind Shiva agreed and put a goat's head on Daksha and revived him. But his dear Sati was lost forever.

Shiva and Parvati

After Sati's death, Lord Shiva became a recluse*. He stayed in deep meditation and did not speak to anyone for years.

King Himavan, who ruled over the great Himalayas was blessed with a daughter, whom he named Parvati. The girl was Sati reborn as Parvati. When she grew up, sage Narada informed Himavan that Parvati would be married to Lord Shiva. So Himavan took

Parvati to Shiva and said, “Oh Lord! It is my humble desire that my daughter serves you.” “Himavan! After Sati’s death, I have not allowed any lady to even come near me or disturb my meditation,” said Shiva.

"Lord! Please give me a chance to serve you and I assure you that I will not disturb your meditation," said Parvati. Shiva could not refuse her pleas, and Parvati began serving Lord Shiva.

Meanwhile, Tarakasura—a powerful demon—knew that Lord Shiva had left all else but meditation and decided to take advantage of his absence. He performed a penance to obtain a boon from Lord Brahma. When Brahma appeared, Tarakasura said, "Lord! Grant me immortality[1]." Brahma replied that no one could be granted such a boon. "If that is so, please grant me the boon that no one other than Lord Shiva's son can kill me," said

Tarakasura, knowing that Shiva would never come out of his meditation and marry anyone. Brahma granted him the boon.

Tarakasura set out to harass all the gods and people on earth. His evil ways tormented everyone. Indra went to Brahma pleading for help. "Lord! It is your boon that has given Tarakasura the power to torment all of us. Please save us from this torture by telling us when Lord Shiva's son will be born," said Indra.

Brahma thought for a while and said, "The time will soon come." Brahma called Kama—the god of love—and said, "Kama, go to mount Kailash and help Lord Shiva find love for Parvati."

Kama went to Kailash with Rati Devi, his wife. He saw that Shiva was deep in meditation and Parvati was sitting by his side making a floral garland. Kama shot his arrow of flowers and Shiva felt a sudden change of heart. There

was a fragrance in the air and Shiva knew that Kama had shot his arrow of love. He opened his eyes in anger and burnt Kama with the fire from his third eye.

Rati Devi was shocked to see her husband raised to ashes. She ran to Indra for help. "It is on Lord Brahma's command that my husband went to Kailash, and Lord Shiva has burnt him to death. Please forgive him and bring

him back to life," she pleaded. Indra approached Shiva with the request. Shiva knew that Kama had not done it to disturb his meditation and

forgave him. He brought him back to life and blessed the couple.

Parvati, who was a witness to such anger by Lord Shiva, decided to leave mount Kailash and go away to another mountain.

But, the gods were worried as Tarakasura's evil ways had not ended. This time, Lord Brahma himself went to Lord Shiva to request him to get married. "Who will marry a sage like me?" asked Shiva. "There is one waiting

to marry you my Lord! It is Parvati," replied Brahma.

Shiva thought for a moment and said, "But I would like to test her devotion." So Shiva sent a few hermits to tell Parvati that Shiva

was not worthy of her. Parvati politely told them that if she would ever marry it would only be Shiva and no one else.

So Shiva decided to disguise himself as an ascetic and went to Parvati himself. "What happiness can a man in a tiger skin and ashes give a lovely woman like you?" he asked

Parvati. "Oh holy one! Do not bring me to a state where I would have to hurt you with my words. Be gone! Shiva is my chosen one, and I cannot think of anyone else," she said.

Shiva assumed his actual form and Parvati was pleased to see him. "It is you!" she cried out in delight. Shiva married Parvati with the blessings of Himavan and his wife Mena Devi. Soon they had a divine child called Subramanya, who ended Tarakasura's evil ways.

* Recluse: Not in contact with anyone.

[1] Immortality: To live on forever.

Shiva: The Greatest of Them All

Brahma is known as the creator of the universe, Vishnu the protector and Shiva, the destroyer. Each of them is respected for their power.

But one day, Lord Brahma was struck with a strange thought, "I am the creator! I actually bring to life everything that exists in this universe. Surely no one can be more powerful

than me.” Unknown to Brahma, Lord Vishnu was also struck with a similar thought. “Brahma might create the universe. But what use is it if I don’t protect what he creates!” he thought. “So I should be the greatest,” thought Vishnu.

Brahma and Vishnu met and started arguing with each other. "I am the greatest," said Vishnu, while Brahma refused to accept Vishnu's supremacy and said, "No! I am the greatest!"

The gods knew that there would be no end to this fight. So they went to Lord Shiva. "Lord! Only you can resolve Vishnu and Brahma's quarrel," they said.

When Shiva reached the spot where Vishnu and Brahma were arguing, they were so immersed in their quarrel that they did not even notice Shiva's entry.

Shiva decided to teach them a lesson and assumed the form of a blazing pillar. "Whoever is the greater of you two will find either the beginning of this pillar or the end of it," said Shiva.

Vishnu assumed the form of a boar and plunged down to find the end of the pillar. Whereas, Brahma assumed the form of a swan and flew high up to find the beginning of the pillar. After traveling for hours, Vishnu could

still not find the end of it. So he decided to give up. However, Brahma, who could also not find the beginning, found a falling Ketaki* flower. "Shiva usually has a ketaki flower on his head. So I must have reached the beginning of the pillar," thought Brahma. He took the flower as proof to show Vishnu that he had indeed seen the beginning.

"I found the beginning and the ketaki flower is witness to that," said Brahma to Vishnu. "Is it true?" asked Vishnu to the flower. "Of course it is," replied the flower.

At that moment Shiva appeared. He was furious with Brahma for lying. "You never saw the beginning and you have lied!" said Shiva angrily. Shiva created a demon called Bhairava with one wave of his hand. "Punish Brahma

for his lie," ordered Shiva. Bhairava cut off Brahma's fifth head[1]. "You will never be worshipped in any temple," said Shiva to Brahma. "And you ketaki! You will never be used for my worship," said Shiva.

"Shiva, you are truly the most powerful of all," said Vishnu with folded hands. "We were foolish to think that we could be greater than you. You are one who does not have a beginning or an end," said Vishnu accepting that Shiva was indeed the greatest of them all.

* Ketaki is known as Keura in Hindi and Screw pine/Umbrella tree in English.

[1] That is how Brahma came to be known for his four heads. There is a pillar at Elephanta caves in Mumbai, Maharashtra, that depicts the burning pillar; Vishnu as a boar going down to find the end of the pillar; and Brahma as a swan flying up to find the beginning of the pillar.

Shiva Gets His Blue Throat

Once, the gods (devas) and the demons (asuras) decided to work together to churn the nectar of immortality from the ocean. They used mount Mandara and Vasuki, the snake to churn the ocean.

"We will not hold the tail of the snake," said the asuras. So they decided to hold the head in the churning. After days of churning, Vasuki starting spewing a deadly poison called Haalahal from its mouth.

The poison was so strong that it spread all over the three worlds and soon, the gods and demons were falling unconscious because of it.

Indra, the king of gods, ran to Lord Shiva to save them all. "I shall always protect those who seek my help," said Shiva and proceeded to the ocean.

He caught all the poison in his hands and drank it. Parvati, who was by his side caught hold of his throat. "Do not swallow it my Lord!" she pleaded. Shiva retained the poison in his throat, which made his throat blue in colour.

Shiva is also known as Neelkanth—the one who has a blue throat.

Shivarathri

There lived a hunter in a small village with his family. He used to hunt animals and birds from the nearby forest. One day, after having walked through the entire forest for a catch, the hunter could not find even one.

Soon it became dark, and the hunter was caught in the forest. He climbed up a tree and took shelter. A short while later, the hunter saw a deer pass by. He took aim at the deer with his bow and arrow. But, to his surprise, the deer spoke to him. The deer said, "Please let me go for now. I will bid farewell to my family and come back here tomorrow night." The hunter took pity and let the deer go.

A few hours passed and the hunter saw another deer pass by. He took aim at the deer, but this time again, the deer spoke. It begged the hunter for time to bid farewell to its family.

"Both the deers were animals, but loved their families. They asked for time to bid farewell. I am a human being and yet never think about my wife and children," thought the hunter.

He spent the whole night atop the tree. With nothing much to do and the full night ahead of him, the hunter kept plucking a few leaves from the tree and dropping them down. The tree was a "Bilva" (Bael) tree and unknown to the hunter, the leaves kept falling on a Shivalinga (Shiva's statue) below the tree.

In the morning, the hunter saw a herd of deers walking towards him. Every deer pleaded to be killed instead of the other. The hunter

was moved by this sight. "I will not kill any of you," said the hunter and climbed down the tree.

He went back to his family a happy and changed man. Years later, when the hunter

died, he was taken to the heavens. The hunter was shocked that a cruel man who had killed so many innocent animals and birds could go to the heavens. But a divine voice told him that he had unknowingly fasted all through

the night—the holy night of Shivarathari (the festival celebrated in the month of February or March every year)—and had also worshipped the idol of Shiva with Bael leaves. “Your act of kindness towards the animals despite being a hunter won the love of the lord,” said the voice.

It is believed that fasting through the night on Shivarathri and worshipping Lord Shiva with Bael leaves ensures luck and prosperity for all the devotees.

Shiva Teaches Humility

King Bhagiratha had a great desire. Bhagiratha's ancestors—the 60,000 sons of King Sagara— had been burnt to ashes by a sage Kapila. He knew that only the purity of mother Ganga could wash away the sins of his ancestors and give them their place in the heavens.

So, Bhagiratha pleaded with mother Ganga to descend to earth. “Mother, only you can bring peace to my ancestors,” he said. “I will be happy to descend to the earth. But there is no one who can control my powerful flow. Also, I live in the heavens where I am pure. If I descend to the earth, I will be defiled,” she replied.

"Mother, all the great sages on earth will keep you pure. I will pray to Lord Shiva to help you in your descent," said Bhagiratha. He performed a penance to please Lord Shiva.

"Your prayers have borne fruit," said Lord Shiva appearing before Bhagiratha. "Tell me what you desire," he asked. "Lord, my ancestors will be purified by the waters of mother Ganga, who has accepted to descend to earth. However, only you can control her powerful

flow. I beseech you to help me," said Bhagiratha. Lord Shiva agreed and the heavens witnessed the event when mother Ganga began her descent to earth.

"Let me show Shiva how powerful my waters are," thought Ganga and flowed down as fast as lightning. But Lord Shiva was too quick for her. Before she knew, she was caught in the matted locks of Lord Shiva.

"Release me oh Lord!" she cried. But Shiva remained silent. Finally, Bhagiratha pleaded with Lord Shiva and he let her flow out of his matted locks on to the earth.